on a road trip

SPY IT! SCORE IT!

Introduction

A road trip can be the start of an adventure, a holiday, a visit to see a friend or relative, or simply a drive out into the countryside. Whatever the occasion, be sure to take i-SPY On A Road Trip with you and you'll have a record of everything you saw.

As you travel around, take time to look out of the window and see all that is around you. There are always masses of things to see wherever you're travelling. Signs along the road give advice, warn of hazards or provide compulsory instructions. You may even be lucky enough to spot some roadside wildlife!

Use your book on all of the road trips you take, but remember not to distract the driver, be sure to wear a seatbelt and make yourself as comfortable as possible.

How to use your i-SPY book

Keep your eyes peeled for the i-SPYs in the book.

If you spy it, score it by ticking the circle or star.

Items with a star are difficult to spot so you'll have to search high and low to find them.

50 POINTS

If there is a question and you know the answer, double your points. Answers can be found at the back of the book (no cheating, please!).

Once you score 1000 points, send away for your super i-SPY certificate. Follow the instructions on page 64 to find out how.

20 MPH speed limit

5 POINTS

30 MPH speed limit

5 POINTS

40 MPH speed limit

5 POINTS

50 MPH speed limit

5 POINTS

60 MPH speed limit

5 POINTS

National speed limit

5 POINTS

Road signs

Watch out for these triangular warning signs.

Cattle

15 POINTS

Horses

15 POINTS

Sheep

15 POINTS

Helicopter

15 POINTS

Roadworks

15 POINTS

Side winds

15 POINTS

Hump bridge

 15 POINTS

Tunnel

 15 POINTS

Riverside bridge

15 POINTS

Pedestrian crossing

15 POINTS

Slippery surface

15 POINTS

Traffic light

 15 POINTS

Road signs

Falling rocks

 10 POINTS

No motorised vehicles

 10 POINTS

No overtaking

 10 POINTS

No cycling

 10 POINTS

No pedestrians

 10 POINTS

No U-turn

 10 POINTS

Red route

Usually in busy city and town centres, these are streets with extra parking restrictions to keep the road free-flowing.

10 POINTS

Congestion zone

15 POINTS

Low emission zone

20 POINTS

7

Road signs

Look out for these brown tourist information signs.

Museum

15 POINTS

Picnic area

10 POINTS

Zoo

25 POINTS

Dry ski slope

TOP SPOT!

35 POINTS

Beach

15 POINTS

Country park

10 POINTS

Heritage site

 20 POINTS

Viewpoint

 10 POINTS

Castle

 15 POINTS

Cricket ground

 TOP SPOT!

 35 POINTS

Campsite

 10 POINTS

Tourist information

 5 POINTS

Road signs

Blue motorway sign

All motorway signs are blue.

5 POINTS

(M40, M1), Watford
(M3, M23)
M25 Gatwick ✈
Heathrow ✈
(Term 4, 5 & Cargo)

The North A1 ✈
Catterick
A6136
Catterick Garrison

Green primary route sign

These are for main (or A) roads all around the country...

5 POINTS

White local route sign

...and these are for local roads.

5 POINTS

Millhouses ↑

← City Centre
A625

Castleton →
A625

10

Pre-Worboys sign

Nearly all UK road signs were modernised in 1964 by the Worboys Committee. A few escaped and are still present today.

35 POINTS

Old-fashioned

You are most likely to find these old fashioned signs in villages.

15 POINTS

Magic roundabout

A few of these complicated junctions exist in the UK. A cluster of small roundabouts surround a major one.

20 POINTS

Road signs

A gradient sign indicates the angle or steepness of a hill or incline. The higher the number, the steeper the hill. Some older road signs indicate the number as a ratio – 1:4 is the same as 25%.

25% gradient

In this case the sign advises the driver that a downhill section of road is approaching.

20 POINTS

30% gradient

In this case, uphill with many other advisory instructions.

25 POINTS

40% gradient

A very steep downhill road.

30 POINTS

Truck route

A sign like this indicates the best route for trucks to take, avoiding smaller side roads and helps prevent congestion.

15 POINTS

Bus lane

Bus lanes ensure that buses can travel freely during the busy rush hours. Often the main sign will be accompanied by another outlining which hours the bus lane operates.

10 POINTS

To the seaport

This way if you are catching a ferry.

15 POINTS

Road signs

Ring road

Many cities and towns have roads around them. This means that heavy traffic can avoid the city centre.

10 POINTS

Diamond diversion

There may be emergency roadworks on a main road. This diamond sign shows a diversion route.

15 POINTS

Footpath

Footpath signs are common in the country and can be seen along the roadside.

10 POINTS

ADUR DISTRICT COUNCIL

Welcome to
the historic town of

SHOREHAM-BY-SEA

Twinned with RIOM, FRANCE & ŻYWIEC POLAND

20 POINTS

Double if the town is twinned
with more than one place

Twinned

Twinned towns or cities have close links or are usually twinned with
similar places in other countries. Some places are twinned with
towns from more than one country. Twinning can be used to promote
tourism between the twinned towns. Over the years, there have
been some fun examples of twinning including the village of Dull in
Perthshire with Boring in Oregon, USA, and Wincanton in Somerset
twinned with Ankh-Morpork from Terry Pratchett's Discworld.

Through the town

Bus stop

You are bound to find a bus stop in a street near you. Some, like this one, show several bus routes...

5 POINTS

Out of order bus stop

...but sometimes the bus stop may have to be taken out of service. This can happen if roadworks are being carried out.

25 POINTS

Park and ride

Many towns and cities encourage motorists to park on the outskirts of town and travel to the centre by bus. 'Park and ride' schemes reduce the amount of city centre traffic.

10 POINTS

Parent and child parking

Most supermarkets have parent and child spaces, located close to the entrance.

10 POINTS

Pay and display

Be sure to pay for parking where you see this sign.

10 POINTS

Have you
PAID
&
DISPLAYED
your ticket ?

POLICE WARNING
Motorists!
Don't leave
valuables
in your car

Avon and Somerset Constabulary
working in partnership with
TOLLGATE SECURITY

Valuables

It is a good idea not to leave valuable items in the car.

10 POINTS

Museum

Museums and galleries can be very popular – you may face a long queue to get in. Be patient – it will be worth it!

10 POINTS

Double if you go in one

Theatre

A trip to the theatre is an exciting adventure.

10 POINTS

Double if you go in one

18

Florist

Many shops have street-side displays showing their wares to foot and car passengers alike. Florists often have particularly pleasant displays.

Car Wash

Car wash

There are different kinds of car washes. The one shown here is an automatic car wash that you drive through. With others, people will wash your car by hand using water jets. At some car washes you are given the water jets to wash the car yourself!

Multiplex cinema

Multiplex cinemas can screen many films at the same time.

10 POINTS

Library

A great place to borrow a book, or use a computer.

10 POINTS

Hotel

Many hotels are grand buildings, sometimes with hundreds of bedrooms, and form part of the local history.

10 POINTS

Monarch statue

Many towns and villages have statues of kings and queens.

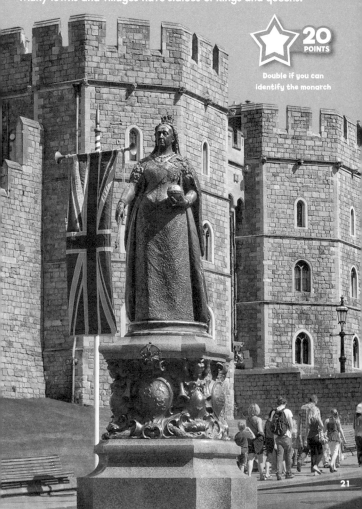

20 POINTS

Double if you can
identify the monarch

Memorial

Memorials are usually erected to remember those who have died in war or in conflict.

15 POINTS

Equestrian statue

Equestrian means 'on horseback' so look for a statue of a rider on a horse.

25 POINTS

Town hall

Town halls are normally grand buildings situated in the centre of town, often in a prominent position or overlooking an important square.

10 POINTS

POSTING BOX

LETTERS
FIRST CLASS

NEWSPAPERS
AND PACKETS

LETTERS
SECOND CLASS

Posting box

It's quite rare to see one of these old-fashioned posting boxes now – you may only find them outside a large town or city post office.

30
POINTS

TOP
SPOT!

Wall clock

35
POINTS

Many town centres throughout the country still have ornate public clocks, often near town halls or other public buildings.

Outdoor fun

Morris dancing

A traditional style dating back hundreds of years, popular at village fêtes.

25 POINTS

Punch and Judy

Good old-fashioned fun! You are most likely to see a Punch and Judy show at the seaside. This tradition dates back over 100 years.

15 POINTS

Balloon seller

Sometimes there are so many balloons that it is difficult to see the balloon seller!

20 POINTS

Tractor

In the countryside you will often see a tractor either at work in a field or occasionally holding up the traffic.

 15 POINTS

Combine harvester

Giant combine harvesters gather in wheat from the crops and bale the straw automatically.

 20 POINTS

Bales

After the grain has been harvested, the straw is left in round or oblong bales in the field.

15 POINTS

25

Farm shop

Farm shops are usually attached to a farm where locally produced meat, vegetables and fruit are sold.

15 POINTS

FARM SHOP

FRESH VEGETABLES
POTATOES
FREE RANGE EGGS

Horsebox

Horseboxes are needed to transport horses around the country and come in many shapes and sizes.

15 POINTS

Roe deer

One of our native deer. Naturally shy, they sometimes run across country roads at night.

25 POINTS

Pony

You can still find wild ponies in several areas of Britain.

20 POINTS

Badger

TOP SPOT!

Sadly, you are most likely to see a dead badger killed on the road, but occasionally they can be spotted alive, by the roadside.

50 POINTS

Roadside wildlife

Fox

Foxes are surprisingly common and often visit towns and gardens at night looking for food.

20 POINTS

Pheasant

Most often spotted strutting around verges and field boundaries. The males are more colourful than the females.

 10 POINTS

Red kite

Brought back from the brink of extinction, red kites can be seen in small flocks in some areas.

25 POINTS

Black-headed gull

Flocks of gulls are often seen following the farmer's plough or at landfill sites looking for food.

 15 POINTS

Unusual vehicles on the road

Dog van

These vehicles have a rooftop air vent to allow the dogs to breathe.

25 POINTS

Skip truck

A great way to dispose of large quantities of waste.

15 POINTS

Concrete mixer

The drum holding the wet concrete rotates during driving to makes sure it doesn't set before being delivered.

20 POINTS

Recovery truck

Essential to keep the roads clear.

15 POINTS

Unusual vehicles on the road

Convertible

A fun way to travel when the sun is shining!

10 POINTS

Kit car

Kit cars are easily spotted as they look different to most other cars on the road and are sometimes referred to as replica cars.

35 POINTS

TOP SPOT!

City bikes

These bikes-for-hire have been introduced to several UK cities and have been a great success. Pick one up at the train station and deposit it at your destination!

10 POINTS

Lorry

Lorries are a common sight on UK roads, picking up
and delivering a wide range of goods. Many lorries
started their journey in other countries and can be
spotted by their different number plates.

10 POINTS

Unusual vehicles on the road

Citroën 2CV

The 'tin snail' was originally designed to carry French country folk and their cargoes of eggs across rutted fields!

25 POINTS

Landrover (series 1)

Many of these very popular off-road vehicles were originally designed for military purposes.

20 POINTS

MGB GT

You may see either an open-top roadster (convertible) or this GT coupe featuring a tailgate rear door.

20 POINTS

VW camper van

You will often find lovingly restored VW vans at surfing beaches or at family picnic spots and viewpoints.

25 POINTS

Ford Anglia

This popular car has found a whole new lease of life since appearing in the *Harry Potter* books.

35 POINTS

TOP SPOT!

Unusual vehicles on the road

Road sweeper

Man-made rubbish like plastic bags and natural debris such as leaves in the autumn gather at the roadside. Vehicles such as this road sweeper use special brushes and vacuums to keep the streets clean.

15 POINTS

Horse and cart

Horses and carts may be used by sightseeing tourists, or sometimes for weddings.

30 POINTS

Wedding car

Wedding cars are easily recognisable due to the ribbons that adorn the bonnet. They are usually either very plush luxury cars or classic cars. Often, the type of car chosen will have significance to the couple getting married.

35 POINTS

TOP SPOT!

Unusual vehicles on the road

Limousine

Hired for special occasions.

15 POINTS

Double if it is pink

Caravan

Caravans and camper vans let you pack up and take your home wherever you like!

10 POINTS

for each

Car or van with trailer

Trailers are a great way to transport boats and canoes.

15 POINTS

Bowls

Bowls are weighted on one side so that they follow a curved line when rolled toward the jack.

15 POINTS

Cricket ground

You may see a game being played at a professional stadium or a more sedate game on a village green.

10 POINTS

Golf course

Golf courses are found all over the country but particularly in the more rural parts of Scotland where the game was invented. Those by the sea are called links courses.

10 POINTS

Sports

Athletics track

You may see a major competition at an athletics track.

20 POINTS

Tennis court

Tennis courts can be found in many parks and in some private gardens!

10 POINTS

Outdoor gym

These are a great way to keep fit and have fun!

15 POINTS

Horse racing track

Horse racing attracts millions of visitors each year. Some courses have special races that are held annually and are shown on TV.

15
POINTS

Ice rink

Your local ice rink may host ice hockey matches or you may simply prefer to skate around to the music.

20
POINTS

Dry ski slope

An ideal way to prepare for skiing on real snow.

TOP
SPOT!

35
POINTS

Stickers and badges

L-plate

The traditional red on white L-plate shows that the driver is a learner.

5 POINTS

P-plate

This P-plate shows that the vehicle is being driven by someone who has recently passed their driving test – a probationary driver.

10 POINTS

Disabled badge sign

Many places such as supermarkets save parking spots near the doors for people who have difficulty getting around – drivers who have a blue badge like this one are allowed to park in these spaces.

5 POINTS

Baby on board

Often people have a 'baby on board' sign on the back windscreen of their car. These help emergency services know to look for a small child in the event of an accident. Many people have more stylised signs saying things like 'little princess on board'. Score for any wording.

BABY
ON BOARD

15 POINTS

International registration

Cars from foreign countries can be identified by their number plates and an international registration badge.

Belgium

B

15 POINTS

France

F

10 POINTS

Germany

D

10 POINTS

Hungary

H

15 POINTS

Ireland

IRL

5 POINTS

Italy

I

15 POINTS

Jersey

25 POINTS

Netherlands

10 POINTS

Norway

15 POINTS

Poland

15 POINTS

Spain

15 POINTS

Switzerland

25 POINTS

Number plates

Since 1963, car registration numbers have denoted the year that the car was registered. Before this, they generally had three numbers and three letters. The letters were the designation of the area or city where the car had first been registered. In 1963, registrations had a letter added to denote the year: ABC 123 A, then in 1964, ABC 123 B and so on. This system lasted until 1983, the last registration in this format being ABC 123 Y. This was followed by putting the letter showing the year at the front of the number plate: A 123 ABC, B 123 ABC for 1984 and so on.

Pre 1963 plate

ABC 123

25 POINTS

From 1963

ABC 123 A

20 POINTS

End of 1983

ABC 123 Y

20 POINTS

From 1983

A 123 ABC

15 POINTS

This lasted until September 2001 when the first of the registration plates we see today appeared with two letters, then two numbers (showing the year) followed by three random letters. Cars are now registered twice a year – in March and September. Cars registered in March use the last two digits of the year (e.g. KX 21 ABC for March 2021), and cars registered in September use the last two digits of the year with 50 added (e.g. KX 71 ABC for September 2021). You will see some 'newer' cars with old, pre-1963 number plates (i.e. ABC 123). This is usually done to personalise the car, perhaps with the owner's initials, and these number plates are referred to as 'private number plates'. You will sometimes see these offered for sale, along with unusual modern number plates.

From 2001

10
POINTS

2008 plate

10
POINTS

2021/2022 plate

10
POINTS

Personalised

10
POINTS

Score for any private or personalised plate

Start of motorway sign

After this point, motorway rules apply.

5 POINTS

No entry sign

Stop! Do not go along this road, cars will be coming the other way.

5 POINTS

Slip road

5 POINTS

If you want to join the motorway, you must first use a short piece of road known as a slip road. This allows you to get up to motorway speed before joining the main carriageway.

Hard shoulder

If a road is classed as a motorway, it usually has a hard shoulder. Traffic is not permitted on this, except in case of breakdown or when instructed to do so.

5 POINTS

No hard shoulder

Some motorways have limited space and do not have any room for a hard shoulder, typically around an obstruction such as a bridge.

10 POINTS

> No hard shoulder for 400 yards

Motorway splits

5 POINTS

Major junctions where motorways split in two or more directions often have direction signs for two miles before to prepare drivers.

Steel central barrier

The central barrier in the middle of the motorway is a safety feature to help prevent cars travelling in opposite directions from hitting each other.

Cat's eyes

Cat's eyes were first used in 1933. Every time a car runs over one it 'cleans' the eye. They mark the centre of the road by reflecting headlights back to the driver at night.

5 POINTS

Direction sign

This sign gives drivers destination information about the next junction.

5 POINTS

Services

It is important to take regular breaks on a long road trip. Motorway service stations offer refreshments and toilet facilities. This sign tells you how far away (and on which motorway) the next service area is.

5 POINTS

Services	
M 4	16 m
M 5 (N)	22 m
M 5 (S)	27 m

M 1
The NORTH
Sheffield 32
Leeds 59

Distance on motorway

It is important to know how far it is to your destination and motorways provide regular updates on distances to the nearest major towns.

5 POINTS

Airport sign

Take this exit for the airport.

10 POINTS

A 45
Birmingham (E)
N.E.C.
Coventry (S & W)

6 ½m

County border

At this point you are passing into a new county.

15 POINTS

Country border

And at this one you are crossing into a new country!

25 POINTS

On the motorway

Don't drive tired

Every year, many accidents are caused by drivers who fall asleep at the wheel. This sign reminds the driver to take a break.

15 POINTS

Gritting

Gritting the roads helps to stop them from freezing in winter.

10 POINTS

SOS phone

If drivers break down, they can use these SOS phones to call for help. They are marked with a unique number so emergency services know where to send assistance.

5 POINTS

9602 B
SOS

Speed camera sign

This is a warning sign to alert drivers there are speed cameras ahead.

5 POINTS

Average speed camera

These cameras read the number plate of passing vehicles and measure their speed over a set distance.

10 POINTS

At the services

moto · MARKS & SPENCER

Ferrybridge services 1½ m

With access to all routes

Services sign

This is one of the signs that informs drivers that the services are approaching.

10 POINTS

Fuel station

You may need to refuel at the service station.

5 POINTS

Refreshments

While you are at the services you many want to buy a drink or snack to take away, or you may have time to sit down and enjoy a meal in the restaurant.

5 POINTS

People shopping

Most services have shops selling all kinds of things.

5 POINTS

Picnic area

If you have brought along your own picnic you could sit outside in the sunshine.

10 POINTS

Roadworks

Works access sign

This is a works site entrance giving access to workers' vehicles only.

5 POINTS

Free recovery

Roadworks are places where it is very easy for traffic to build up so to help move blockages quickly, if you break down while travelling through roadworks, a recovery truck will take you to safety for no charge.

5 POINTS

Night-time works
14 July to 26 July

Expect delays

Delays possible until...

Wherever there are roadworks, there are often delays.

5 POINTS

Diggers

○ **5** POINTS

Track diggers like this one are always used on major roadworks and road building schemes, so that huge chunks of material can be dug out in one go and the construction work can be carried out with the minimum of delay.

Road rollers

Used to make the road surface smooth and flat.

○ **10** POINTS

Roadworks

Narrow lanes

While repairs are taking place, there is often limited space so lane width is reduced.

5 POINTS

Lane closed

Mobile lane closure signs warn drivers to keep to one side of the road.

10 POINTS

Cones

Cones are common sights on UK roads when roadworks are going on. They can be used to keep vehicles in lanes or to cut off some exits entirely.

5 POINTS

Car badges

Almost every car carries a logo, usually positioned on the front grille and the boot. Here are some that you might see.

Alfa Romeo

 15 POINTS

Aston Martin

 30 POINTS

Audi

 10 POINTS

BMW

 15 POINTS

59

Car badges

TOP SPOT!

Ferrari

35 POINTS

Ford

10 POINTS

Mitsubishi
15 POINTS

Mercedes-Benz

10 POINTS

Nissan

 **10** POINTS

Peugeot

10 POINTS

Porsche

 30 POINTS

Renault

 10 POINTS

Car badges

Smart **20** POINTS

Seat **10** POINTS

Volvo **10** POINTS

Toyota  **10** POINTS

Index

i-SPY How to get your i-SPY certificate and badge

Let us know when you've become a super-spotter with 1000 points and we'll send you a special certificate and badge!

Here's what to do!

- Ask an adult to check your score.

- Apply for your certificate at www.collins.co.uk/i-SPY (If you are under the age of 13 we'll need a parent or guardian to do this).

- We'll email your certificate and post you a brilliant badge!